I really don't know why: a sibling song to autism

Written and illustrated by Haitham Al-Ghani

The National
Autistic Society

My brother's different,

I really don't know why.

My brother's different,

He likes to scream and cry.

My brother's different,

He likes to line up toys,

And if I try to play with him,

He makes a lot of noise!

My brother's different,

He always eats the same food,

If mother changes his routine,

He gets in a terrible mood.

He doesn't seem to understand,

And yet I know he speaks,

And if I try to explain to him,

He put his fingers in his ears and shrieks!

My brother's different,

He always takes my things,

If I tell my mum on him,

She only smiles and sings.

My brother's different,

He talks such boring stuff.

Mother said I should be patient,

But it really is quite tough.

My brother's different,

He likes to watch TV,

But if we are watching Robin Hood,

He doesn't care about me!

When we get to his favourite bit,

He jumps up and shouts with glee,

Then he presses rewind.

He never thinks of me!

My brother's different,

He's just mad about trains,

We visit boring stations,

Even when it rains.

My brother's different,

He doesn't like the bath,

He runs around without his clothes,

He really makes me laugh!

My brother's different,

He flaps his hands in the air,

He does it in Marks & Spencer,

People don't half stare!

My brother's different,

I really don't know why,

My brother's different,

He's an autistic guy.

Other books about autistic spectrum disorders

The National Autistic Society publishes many helpful books for the parents and families of children with autism.

Here are a few helpful titles

Autism: how to help your young child
Leicestershire County Council and Fosse Health Trust
£10.99

It can get better... dealing with common behaviour problems in young autistic children
Paul Dickinson and Liz Hannah
Illustrations by Steve Lockett
£5.00

Asperger syndrome – practical strategies for the classroom: a teacher's guide
Leicester City Council and Leicestershire County Council
£10.99

My brother is different: a book for young children who have a brother with autism
Louise Gorrod
Illustrations by Beccy Carver
£4.99

My sister is different: book for young children who have a sister with autism
Written and illustrated by Sarah Tamsin Hunter
£4.99

My special brother Rory
Ellie Fairfoot aged $6\frac{1}{2}$ and Jenny Mayne (Ellie's mum)
Illustrated by Ellie Fairfoot
£2.99

All these books and many more are available from the NAS distributor:
Central Books Ltd, 99 Wallis Road, London E9 5LN
Tel: 0845 458 9911
Fax: 0845 458 9912
Or order online @ www.autism.org.uk/pubs